THE THREE LITTLE PIGS

Axel Scheffler

Retold by Axel Scheffler and Alison Green

One day, Mother Pig said to her three piglets: "You are fine, grown-up piglets now. It's time you went out into the world to seek your fortune!"

The little pigs weren't sure they liked that idea, but they did as they were told.

The first little pig trotted down the road. He hadn't gone far when he bumped into a man carrying a bale of straw.

"Excuse me," said the piglet, "please may I have your straw, so I can build myself a house?"

"Of course," said the man, kindly, and the little pig built himself a cosy home.

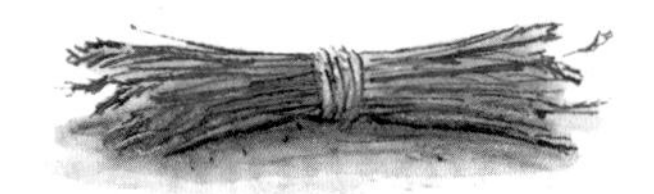

Just then, a wicked wolf rapped at the door.
"Little pig! Let me in!" he growled.

"By the hairs on my chinny-chin-chin, I WON'T let you in!" squeaked the little pig.

"Then I'll huff and I'll puff and I'll blow your house down!" said the wolf. And he huffed and he puffed and he blew down the little house of straw!

The little piglet ran back to his mum as fast as his trotters would carry him.

The second little pig skipped down the road, and bumped into a man carrying a bundle of sticks.

"Excuse me," said the piglet, "please may I have your sticks, so I can build myself a house?"

"You may indeed," said the man, kindly, and the little pig built himself a very neat home.

But who should come by again but the wicked wolf? "Little pig! Let me in!" he growled.

"By my grandfather's curly-whirly tail, I WON'T let you in!" squeaked the second little pig.

"Then I'll huff and I'll puff and I'll blow your house down!" said the wolf. And he huffed and he puffed and he blew down the little house of sticks!

The second little pig ran back to his mum even faster than his brother.

The third little pig strutted down the road, and bumped into a man pushing a barrowful of bricks.

"Excuse me," said the piglet, "please may I have your bricks, so I can build myself a house?"

"You are most welcome, young pig," said the man, kindly, and the little pig built himself a very smart home indeed.

In no time at all, the wicked wolf rapped on the door. "Little pig! Let me in!" he growled.

"By my grandmother's snuffly-wuffly snout, I WON'T let you in!" declared the third little pig, bold as brass.

"Then I'll huff and I'll puff and I'll blow your house down!" said the wolf. And the wolf began to huff and puff. He huffed and puffed as hard as he could.

But he just couldn't blow down the sturdy little house of bricks.

The wolf was all puffed out now, but he still wanted to eat the plump little piglet. So he said: "Little pig, there's a field of tasty turnips over the hill. Why don't we go and pick some tomorrow morning?"

The little pig liked turnips. "Sounds good to me," he said. "What time will you call for me?"

"At six on the dot," said the wolf, and away he went, licking his lips.

At five o'clock next morning, the little pig sprang out of bed. He ran over the hill and found the field of turnips. Then he picked the biggest, tastiest ones he could find, and trotted back home.

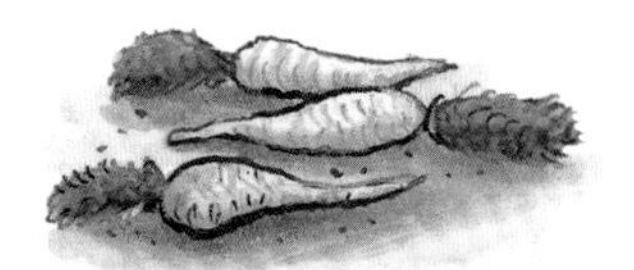

At six on the dot, the wolf rapped on the door: "Little pig, are you ready?"

"Ready?" said the piglet. "I picked my turnips hours ago."

The wolf was very cross. He'd need another plan to catch this piglet. So he said: "Little pig, there's an amazing apple tree over the meadow. If you promise not to trick me again, I'll come by tomorrow at five, and we can pick some together."

The little pig liked apples. "Sounds good to me," he said.

At four o'clock next morning, the little pig raced off to find the amazing apple tree. But when he clambered up it, he saw the wicked wolf approaching.

The wolf was cross that he'd been tricked again, but he tried not to show it. "Nice apples, aren't they?" he said.

"Very nice!" said the piglet. "I'll throw you one. Catch!"

He tossed an apple high into the air. As the wolf scrambled to catch it, the little pig quickly scampered home.

Next day, the wicked wolf called by again, and rapped on the little pig's door.

"Little pig!" he said. "It's the Summer Fair in town today. Won't you come with me?"

"I'd love to," said the little pig. "What time shall we go?"

"At three o'clock sharp," replied the wolf.

Once again, the piglet set off early. He trotted to the fair and bought himself a very fine butter churn. But just as he was about to leave, he saw the angry wolf striding towards him.

There was nowhere else to hide, so the little pig jumped inside his butter churn, which toppled over and rolled higgledy-piggledy all the way down the hill.

When the wolf saw the butter churn tumbling towards him, he was so frightened he forgot all about the Summer Fair. He kicked up his paws and ran.

The next time the wolf went to the little pig's house, he told him all about his lucky escape.

"Haha!" laughed the piglet. "That was me! I jumped inside my butter churn when I saw you coming, and rolled down the hill after you."

The wolf was really angry now. He raged and roared, and said, "Right, little pig! I'm going to climb down your chimney. And when I get down there, I'm going to snap you up whole!"

When the little pig heard that, he hung his big cooking pot over the fire, ready to catch the wolf. Down climbed the wolf. But when he felt the hot steam tickling his toes, he scrambled straight back up the chimney, scooted home, and vowed that he'd never try and eat a piglet again.

As for the little pig, he was very hungry after all his adventures. He made himself a huge pot of turnip soup with plenty of pepper, and he ate up every last drop.

Published in the UK by Alison Green Books, 2022
An imprint of Scholastic

Euston House, 24 Eversholt Street, London, NW1 1DB
Scholastic Ireland, 89E Lagan Road, Dublin Industrial
Estate, Glasnevin, Dublin, D11 HP5F

First published in German under the title:
Die drei Kleinen Schweinchen und der böse Wolf
Published by arrangement with Julius Beltz GmbH & Co. KG.

ISBN: 978 0702 30784 3

A CIP catalogue record for this book is
available from the British Library.

Printed in China

Paper made from wood grown in sustainable
forests and other controlled sources.

9 8 7 6 5 4 3 2 1

www.scholastic.co.uk